1001 RIDDLES FOR CHILDREN

1001 RIDDLES
FOR CHILDREN

Compiled and Illustrated

By

GEORGE L. CARLSON

PLATT & MUNK, Publishers

NEW YORK

FOREWORD

All children love riddles. In this collec-
tion are one thousand and one riddles on
almost every subject. Care has been taken
to select those riddles of particular interest
for children. Any riddles that might be considered objectionable have been eliminated.

An amusing game can be played by select-
ing ten or more riddles to be answered by
the contestants. Count 10 for each correct
answer. The person having the highest
score wins.

This book is both entertaining and educa-
tional and will delight children of all ages.
It is ideal for party games and rainy days.

1001 RIDDLES FOR CHILDREN

1. With what two animals do you always go to bed?
2. When is a boy not a boy?
3. How many legs has a sheep if you call a tail a leg?
4. Which eats more grass, black sheep or white?
5. What most frequently becomes a woman?

6. When does a boy sneeze?
7. How many hairs in a Bunny Rabbit's tail?
8. Why are bad children like old trunks?
9. What is the difference between a donkey and a postage stamp?
10. To what man do men always take their hats off?

11. How do we know that Bunnies gossip?
12. When is a bump like a hat?
13. What American has had the largest family?
14. What question can never be answered by "Yes"?
15. When the clock strikes 13, what time is it?

16. When will water stop running down hill?
17. What changes a lad into a lady?
18. What is the smallest bridge in the world?
19. Who was the best business woman in the Bible?
20. What is higher without the head than with the head?

21. In what month do girls talk the least?
22. Why do we look over a stone wall?
23. What is good for a bald head?
24. Why is your hand like a hardware store?
25. When is the worst weather for rats and mice?

26. How many soft-boiled eggs could the giant Goliath eat on an empty stomach?
27. How long should a man's legs be to be most serviceable?
28. Why don't women become bald as soon as men?
29. What is it that has four legs and only one foot?

30. What is that which is bought by the yard and worn by the foot?
31. What is that which a young lady looks for, but does not wish to find?
32. What can you put up a spout down that you can't put down a spout up?

33. Why did the jelly roll?
34. What is the ugliest hood ever worn?
35. What is the best key to a good dinner?
36. Why is your nose not 12 inches long?
37. How does a boy look when you hurt him?

38. When is a man like a snake?
39. What are a person's last teeth called?
40. Where is the west side of a boy's trousers?
41. Why do we buy clothes?
42. How many peas go into a pot?
43. What makes a road broad?
44. When are cooks cruel?

45. Name a lock no one can pick.
46. Though I dance at a ball, yet I am nothing at all. What am I?
47. In what place did the rooster crow when all the world heard him?
48. What makes a pair of shoes?
49. Why is a dirty rug like a bad boy?

50. What is the best way to raise strawberries?
51. Which is the favorite land of small children?
52. Why does a student never lead a quiet life?
53. How many balls of twine would it take to reach to the moon?
54. What is the end of everything?

55. Why is the crow the bravest of all birds?
56. How can a cat go into a cellar with four feet and come back with eight?
57. What was Joan of Arc made of?
58. When are you a country in South America?

59. Which is heavier, a half or a full moon?
60. How far can you go into the woods?
61. How long is a string?
62. What is a good thing to keep in the summer time?
63. Why is a hen sitting on a fence like a cent?

64. Who was the greatest actor in the Bible?
65. Why are the western prairies so flat?
66. Name the ugliest tree.
67. Which man shaves twenty or more times a day?
68. What is full of holes and yet holds water?

69. What do we have on Christmas Day that we don't have any other day in the year?
70. Why is a quarrel like a bargain?
71. What does everybody give and few take?
72. What is it that is so brittle that even to name it is to break it?

73. When is a black dog not a black dog?
74. What do liars do after death?
75. Why does a donkey prefer thistles to oats?
76. What key is the hardest to turn?
77. When did Moses sleep five in a bed?

78. When may a man call his wife "honey"?
79. What is yours, and used by others more than yourself?
80. Which is the oldest tree?
81. What kind of men usually go to heaven?
82. What goes up and never goes down?

83. What flower does a person carry around all year?
84. What has four wheels and flies?
85. What ant is the youngest?
86. When is it a good thing to lose your temper?
87. What is taken from you before you get it?

88. When is a boy like a pony?
89. What bird is very rude?
90. How do you make a maltese cross?
91. What makes a coach dog spotted?
92. What goes uphill and downhill, and always stays in the same place?

93. What falls often but never gets hurt?
94. What pen should never be used for writing?
95. How can a man be tall and short at the same time?
96. Who was Jonah's teacher?
97. Why is a bad schoolboy like a postage stamp?

98. What has eighteen legs and catches flies?
99. On which side of a country church is the graveyard always situated?
100. The more you take away the larger it grows. What is it?
101. What is larger when cut at both ends?

102. What flowers are kissable?
103. When are boys like bears?
104. What is the best thing out?
105. How did Jonah feel when the whale swallowed him?
106. What two flowers should decorate a menagerie?
107. When is a bright idea like a clock?

108. Why is the position of the President of the United States like a back tooth?
109. A blind beggar had a brother and the brother died; the man that died had no brother. What was the beggar?
110. Why is snow like a maple tree?

111. When is a piece of wood like a queen?
112. How can you be sure the engine in your car isn't missing?
113. A slender body, a tiny eye, no matter what happens, I never cry. What am I?
114. What is the difference between an elephant and a flea?

115. What room can no one enter?
116. In what kind of cord is it impossible to tie a knot?
117. What driver never gets arrested?
118. Why is an infant like a diamond?
119. Who was the straightest man in the Bible?

120. What is the age of communication?
121. What does a stone become when in the water?
122. When is a lamp not a lamp?
123. Three men were under one umbrella but none of them got wet. How did they do it?
124. What goes around a button?

125. Why can't a cook swallow his apron?
126. When is a woman dressed like an Indian chief wearing his war bonnet?
127. Why is a plum-pudding like the ocean?
128. When is butter like Irish children?

129. When is a restaurant like a woodshed?
130. Why is coffee like an axe with a dull edge?
131. What fruit is on a cent?
132. What is a bad thing to get into?
133. What tune makes everybody glad?

134. Where should you feel for the poor?
135. What is the difference between the sidewalk and a street car?
136. If you go for ten cents worth of long, thin tacks, what do you want them for?
137. What is a bare-faced liar?

138. What does the artist like to draw best?
139. When are robes like water?
140. Why is the telegraph like a musical director?
141. Why is it that whenever you are looking for anything, you will always find it in the last place you look?

142. What is the difference between a deer fleeing from
hunters and a midget witch?

143. Which is most valuable, a
paper dollar bill, or a silver
dollar?

144. What trembles at each breath
of air; yet it can bear the
heaviest burdens?

145. Why are strawberries in winter like a pair of stags?

146. Why is the sun like a good loaf
of bread?

147. Why should potatoes grow
better than other vegetables?

148. What is the difference between a hungry man and a
glutton?

149. When is a door not a door?

150. If your uncle's sister is not
your aunt, what relation is she
to you?

151. Why do chimneys smoke?

152. Why is an old man like a window?

153. What asks no questions but
requires many answers?

154. When is water like fat?
155. Which is the miss whose company no one wants?
156. When have elephants eight feet?
157. When is water like a tiger?
158. Why couldn't they play cards on the ark?
159. Why is a wig like a lie?

160. When a boy falls, what does he fall against?
161. Fashions change but what can a person wear that is never out of style?
162. What changes a pear into a pearl?
163. When is an ear of corn like a question?

164. Why did the lobster blush?
165. Who always goes to bed with his shoes on?
166. What roof covers the most noisy tenant?
167. What is a put-up job?
168. What is there about a house that seldom falls, but never hurts the tenant when it does?

169. What name besides Anna reads the same both ways?
170. What question is that to which you positively must answer yes?
171. Why is any empty purse always the same?
172. Which is the left side of a plum pudding?

173. When is music like vegetables?
174. Why should a doctor never be seasick?
175. Who is a painstaking man?
176. Who always enjoys poor health?
177. Why is steel trap like the measles?

178. What is there in your house that ought to be looked into?
179. Why is a sheet of postage stamps like distant relatives?
180. What is the right kind of timber for castles in the air?
181. What is that which works when it plays and plays when it works?
182. What is the difference between a bankrupt and a feather bed?
183. What is the highest public building in your city?

184. Why should a housekeeper never put the letter M into her refrigerator?

185. What is the difference between a new five-cent piece and an old dime?

186. When is an umbrella like a person just getting over an illness?

187. Why is the hand of the Statue of Liberty only eleven inches long?

188. Why should a man always wear a watch when he travels in a desert?

189. What is that which every living person has seen, but will never see again?

190. Why are fishermen and shepherds like beggars?

191. Up and down, up and down, touching neither sky nor ground. What is it?

192. What happens when a light falls into the water at an angle of forty-five degrees?

193. What would happen if a girl swallowed her spoon?
194. What is the difference between a young girl and an old hat?
195. Which is the only way a leopard can change his spots?
196. What are the two smallest things mentioned in the Bible?
197. What is that which never uses its teeth for eating purposes?
198. What are the most disagreeable articles for a man to keep on hand?
199. What is the proper length for a lady's skirt?
200. When butter is worth twenty cents a pound, what will a ton of coal come to?
201. What is the worst kind of fare for a man to live on?
202. If a farmer can raise 250 bushels in dry weather, what can he raise in wet weather?

203. When is a chair like a dress?
204. What table has not a leg to stand on?
205. When is it right for you to lie?
206. What roof never keeps out the wet?
207. Why is a young lady like a hinge?

208. What is that which is put on a table, and cut, but never eaten?
209. When may a chair be said to dislike you?
210. What are the most wonderful things ever built?
211. Why is the letter G like the sun?

212. What coin is double its value when "half" is deducted?
213. Why are doctors sometimes wicked men?
214. What is the pain of which everyone makes light?
215. When does one become soured?
216. What is always behind time?
217. How far is it from March to June?

218. Why is there no such thing as a whole day?

219. Why may carpenters reasonably believe there is no such thing as stone?

220. When does a farmer perform a miracle?

221. When is an artist dangerous?

222. Why is a young lady dependent upon the letter Y?

223. What man in the Bible was the busiest doctor?

224. Why is your eye like a boy being whipped?

225. What kind of ears does an engine have?

226. What has a mouth but never eats?

227. What have feet but cannot walk?

228. What is the last thing you take off before going to bed?

229. Why is an elephant an unwelcome caller?

230. What is always at the head of fashion, yet always out of date?

231. What is the difference between a coat and a baby?

232. When may a man's coat pocket be empty, and yet have something in it?

233. Who sounded the first bell?

234. What is the difference between a boy outside a movie and one inside?

235. When was beef the highest that it has ever been?

236. How many does daddy, mother and baby make?

237. Which is the largest room in the world?

238. What relation is the door-mat to the scraper?

239. What is the best remedy for a smokey chimney?

240. Which is better, an old ten dollar bill or a new one?

241. Why should an artist never be short of cash?

242. Why is a fretful man like a hard-baked loaf?

243. When is a nutmeg like a prison window?

244. Why will a traveler never starve in the desert?
245. Where would you send a man to get an appetite?
246. What comes after cheese?
247. Why does a waxed floor remind you of music?
248. Where does Thursday come before Wednesday?

249. Why are washerwomen great travelers?
250. How would you speak of a tailor when you did not remember his name.
251. Why should a greedy man wear a plaid vest?
252. When is a lamp in bad humor?
253. Why is the letter A like a honey-suckle?

254. What is the difference between a ballet-dancer and a duck?
255. When is a circus-ground like a ship?
256. When is a boat like a heap of snow?
257. What age do most girls wish to attain?

258. When is a girl not a girl?
259. Why is the letter Y like a young spendthrift?
260. Who is most likely to become a fair-haired woman?
261. Who was older, David or Goliath?
262. When do you have four hands?
263. What have eyes but cannot see?

264. Why are children like fountains?
265. What is it that every American man used to be?
266. Why is a poor friend better than a rich one?
267. When is a rope like a child at school?

268. When may a person be said to breakfast before he gets up?
269. What table is all paper?
270. Why are lazy persons' beds too short for them?
271. What is the height of folly?
272. Why would it be better if needle were spelled with an "I"?

273. What is the surest way to double your money?

274. What is better than presence of mind in a railway accident?

275. When does a regiment undergo an operation?

276. When do broken bones begin to make themselves useful?

277. What gives a cold, and pays the doctor?

278. What is it when once lost you can never find again?

279. Why doesn't the clock strike 13?

280. Why is a colt like an egg?

281. Where was Solomon's temple?

282. When is a plant like a hog?

283. On what toe does a corn never come?

284. Why is a story writer a very peculiar creature?

285. Why is a crash of thunder like a jeweler?

286. When does a public speaker steal lumber?

287. When does a tailor serve his customers both well and ill?

ALL EARRINGS ARE MADE HERE

288. What is the difference between a lady and a postage stamp?

289. Why is a ship the most polite thing in the world?

290. What miss is always making blunders?

291. When is a river like the letter T?

292. What must one do to have soft hands?

293. What is the best thing to put into pies?

294. What is the difference between a U. S. President and an old hat?

295. What smells most in a perfumer's shop?

296. Why can't the world ever come to an end?

297. On what point of land should a Greenlander stand to say "goodby"?

298. Why does an Indian wear feathers in his hair?

299. When is the soup likely to run out of the saucepan?

300. What is the difference between here and there?

301. Where can happiness always be found?
302. What is the best and cheapest light?
303. If butter is $1 a pound in Chicago, what are window panes in New York?
304. Name something that can sing and has eight legs.

305. For what profession are the members of a college boat crew best fitted?
306. When is a doctor most annoyed?
307. Why does a person who is sick lose his sense of touch?
308. What is the difference between a mother and a barber?

309. If you see a man scratching his head, what time is it?
310. When is a clock dangerous?
311. Why must chimney-sweeping be a very agreeable business?
312. When is the wind like a wood-chopper?
313. How does an auctioneer look when conducting a sale?

314. Why is not distance at sea measured by miles as it is on land?
315. Why is a bad pin like a broken lead pencil?
316. When was pork first introduced into the Navy?
317. When are eyes not eyes?
318. Why didn't the last dove return to the ark?

319. Do you know anything that has four eyes?
320. Riddle me, riddle me, ree. What is that over your head and under your hat?
321. Why does Uncle Sam wear red - white - and - blue suspenders?

322. When are you most likely to see through a man?
323. Which President wore the largest hat?
324. What goes all the way from Boston to Baltimore without moving?
325. What most resembles the half of an orange?

326. When is an apple like something else?

327. What was the largest island before Australia was discovered?

328. Why is Massachusetts like a statue?

329. What shape is a kiss?

330. What part of London is in France?

331. How do sailors know Long Island?

332. Spell "enemy" in three letters.

333. When is it easy to read in the woods?

334. No matter how smart you are, there is one thing you will always overlook, what is it?

335. What is the first thing a gardener sets in his garden?

336. What does an iron-clad vessel of war, with four inches of steel plating and all her guns on board, weigh just before starting on a cruise?

337. How can five people divide five cookies so that each gets a cookie and yet one cookie remains on the plate?

338. What is the difference between a watchmaker and a jailer?

339. What is it that has a face, but no head, hands, but no feet; yet travels everywhere and is usually running?

340. What flower would remind you of a certain animal that took a great deal of care about his personal appearance?

341. Pretend that you have three doorways to your house with a lamp set over each one, if, on some dark night you have only one match for the three lamps, which will you light first?

342. Why are trees in winter like troublesome visitors?

343. What goes under the water, over the water, yet never touches the water?

344. What is that which no man wishes to have, yet no man wishes to lose?

345. Born at the same time as the world, destined to live as long as the world, and yet never five weeks old?

346. What is it that a person can place in his right hand which cannot be placed in his left hand?
347. If a man sent his son to college these days and paid a thousand dollars a year to put him through, how much change might he get back?
348. Why are the legs of an ill-bred fellow like an organ-grinder?
349. Why is a good speller in a spelling match like a glass of champagne?
350. What is the difference between the North Pole and the South Pole?
351. Why are not fares collected from policemen on street cars?

352. When is a ship at sea not on the water?
353. Which is bigger, Mr. Bigger or Mr. Bigger's baby?
354. Why is the letter E always grouchy?
355. Which is the strongest day of the week?
356. Why is a bubble like a bruise?

357. Which is the best life preserver on a battlefield?
358. I have hands, but no fingers; no bed, but a tick.
359. What is it we all say we will do, recommend others to do, and yet no one ever has done?
360. Why is a shoemaker like a true lover?

361. What is the difference between an organist and his influenza?
362. What is grass green?
363. Why are country girls' cheeks like a good cotton dress?
364. Why are troubles like babies?
365. Why is a lead pencil like a naughty child?

366. How long did Cain hate his brother?

367. What is the difference between a bottle of medicine and a bad boy?

368. Why do we all go to bed?

369. How can you always have friends?

370. What gates are like church bells?

371. What goes upstairs on their heads?

372. What table articles are chips from the old block?

373. What plant stands for four?

374. When does a talkative woman hold her jaw?

375. What word will, if you take away the first letter, make you sick?

376. If a man smashed a clock, would he be convicted of killing time?

377. What comes after buttermilk?

378. Why is a ferry boat like a good rule?

379. What key in music will make a good officer?
380. When is it difficult to get one's watch out of one's pocket?
381. Why is a watermelon filled with water?
382. What time of the day was Adam created?
383. Which is the most dangerous bat that flies in the air?

384. On what day of the year do women talk the least?
385. Why are riddles like goods from another country?
386. What is the most warlike nation?
387. What makes people bald-headed?
388. If a blue stone fell into the Red Sea, what would happen?

389. What vegetable is unpopular on board ship?
390. What chins are never shaved?
391. Why is an old coat like an iron kettle?
392. When must your shoes be left outside of your hotel?

393. If a tree were to break a window, what would the window say?

394. What goes through a door but never goes in or comes out?

395. What islands should have good singers?

396. What is the most difficult train to catch?

397. Why is there nothing so modest as a watch?

398. What professional men generally work with a will?

399. Why does a railroad gateman punch a hole in your ticket?

400. What is the difference between 16 ounces of lead and a pianist?

401. What is everything doing at the same time?

402. Why is a ladder like a prize fight?

403. What is that which nobody wishes to have and nobody likes to lose?

404. What proves sailors to be very careless?

405. Where did Noah strike the first nail in the ark?

406. What bird would be supposed to lift the heaviest weight?

407. What does a tooth have that a tree has?

408. What is it that cannot run, though it has three feet?

409. What islands are good to eat?

410. What fruit is mentioned most in history?

411. Which is the best land for young children?

412. What is it that runs all the way betwen two towns but never moves?

413. What is the difference between a sewing machine and a kiss?

414. What increases its value one-half when turned upside down?

415. Plant the setting sun, and what will come up?

416. What kind of doctor would a duck make?

417. Why is a book like a king?

418. How would you increase the speed of a slow boat?

419. I'll tell you something that will tickle you. What?

420. What is the highest pleasure you can think about?

421. Why are passengers in airplanes so polite to each other?

422. Why does an onion resemble a ringing bell?

423. What is the difference between a cat and a match?

424. Why do ducks and geese fly North in the Springtime?

425. How can you make one pound of green tea go as far as five pounds of black?

426. Why does lightning turn milk sour?

427. Why is a game of baseball like a buckwheat cake?

428. When is a cigar like a shoulder of pork?

429. Why is this book like a tomato?

430. Spell hard butter with four letters.

431. What is it that stays hot in a refrigerator?

432. How many boys does it take to make a loaf?

433. Can you think of any kind of vegetable that won't grow in sandy soil?

434. If Ireland should sink, what would float?

435. What word do most people like best?

436. When were there only two vowels?

437. What is the value of the moon?

438. What is behind a star?

439. What is the difference between the rising sun and the setting sun?

440. Who is least likely to put on too much weight?

441. When is a boxer's eye like a barrel?

442. Why is a freed prisoner like a gun?

443. Why do architects make excellent actors?

444. Why is a butcher's cart like his stockings?
445. When is a lover like a tailor?
446. What is the difference between an elevator and the man who runs it?
447. What is the easiest thing to part with in hot weather?
448. What is worse than raining cats and dogs?

449. What has a bed, but never sleeps?
450. What did Paul Revere say when he finished his famous ride?
451. Why does a hen lay an egg?
452. What turned the roadway on Manhattan Island into Broadway?

453. What tricks are most common in New York in March?
454. Why is a false friend like the letter P?
455. Why are soldiers like the rocks in a mine?
456. On which side does a chicken have the most feathers?

457. Why can't it rain for two days continually?

458. Why is a new-born baby like a gale of wind?

459. What is the middle letter of the A B C's?

460. Why is paper like a beggar?

461. What contains more feet in winter than in summer?

462. What is that we often return and never borrow?

463. What is it we often see made, but never see it after it is made?

464. Why is it foolish to teach the Indian to read?

465. Why is a watchdog bigger by night than by day?

466. When is a blue book not a blue book?

467. What speaks every language?

468. When was B the first letter in the Alphabet?

469. Who handles more letters in a day than a postman?

470. Why may a beggar wear a very short coat?

471. Any difference between a milkmaid and a sea-swallow?
472. In what line of trade do you always find things dull?
473. If the railroad is 40 years old, and the engine 30, how old is the engineer?
474. What fish may be said to be out of place?

475. Why do American soldiers never run away?
476. What was Hobson's choice?
477. Why are some married men like candles?
478. When is a theatrical manager like an astronomer?
479. When does an automobile go exactly as fast as a train?

480. What kind of paper tells you who you are?
481. What has a hand but can't scratch itself?
482. Why is a race-horse like a leaky barrel?
483. If you had a box of candles and no matches, how would you light them?

484. Why is a madman equal to two men?
485. What always goes with a wagon that is no part of it and of no use to it?
486. What is the difference between a bee and a donkey?
487. Why is a tree like a dog?
488. How can we become wiser from a box of pins?

489. What well-known animal drives an automobile?
490. Why do birds clean out a fruit tree so quickly?
491. What makes an empty match box superior to any other?
492. Why are guns like trees?
493. Which pine has the longest needles?

494. What kind of servants are best for hotels?
495. Where is the largest diamond in Boston kept?
496. When does even the bravest heart turn to stone?
497. What is it that you cannot see, but is always before you?

498. Why is a pair of skates like an apple?

499. How can hunters find their game in the woods?

500. What does a yawning policeman resemble?

501. Why is a crown prince like a cloudy day?

502. A houseful, a roomful, can't catch a spoonful.

503. Why does a milkman have a white horse?

504. Why would a barber rather shave six Americans than one foreigner?

505. What is the best way to turn people's heads?

506. Why does the bell make more noise than the cook?

507. What is the difference between a hen and an idle musician?

508. Why can't we send any more dispatches to Washington?

509. What is that which though black enlightens the world?

510. What is the difference between a professional musician and one that hears him?

511. If you saw a counterfeit bill on the sidewalk and walked by it without picking it up, why would you be arrested?

512. If you can buy eight eggs for twenty-six cents, how many can you buy for a cent and a quarter?

513. There is a girl that works in a candy store in Boston who is 5 feet 11 inches tall, has a waist measure of 42 inches and wears a number 9 shoe. What do you think she weighs?

514. What is the difference between a mouse and a young lady?

515. Why is opening a letter like taking a very queer method of getting into a room?

516. Take away my first letter, I remain unchanged; take away my second letter, I'm still the same; take away all my letters and I still continue unchanged.

517. Down on our farm we had a hen that laid an egg six inches long; can you beat that?

518. Instead of complaining when it rains, we should do as they do in China, and what is that?

519. If one horse is in a stockpen and one is running loose down the road, which horse is singing "Don't fence me in"?

520. Why is the telephone company not going to have telephone poles any longer?

521. Why is a loaf of bread on the top of the Empire State Building like a racehorse?

522. What is that which, supposing its greatest width to be four inches, length nine inches, and depth three inches, contains a solid foot?

523. What is that which is too much for one, enough for two, but nothing at all for three?

524. Why are complaints of married people like the noise of the waves on the shore?

525. What is filled every morning and emptied every night except once a year when it is filled at night and emptied in the morning?

526. If you were locked in a room that had in it only a calendar and a bed, what would you do for food?

527. When was tennis mentioned in the Bible?

528. Why does a dog turn around three times before lying down?

529. In what time do people do all their talking?

530. Why is the letter R most important to young people?

531. Why is "A" like twelve o'clock?

532. Of what trade is the President of the United States?

533. Which loom does a weaver like best?

534. What's all over the house?

535. What is the difference between a goose and an author?

536. What is a word of five letters which, when you take away two only one remains?

537. Why is a healthy person like the United States?

538. Why is a drawn tooth like a thing forgotten?

539. What is the key-note to a good manner?

540. Why does time fly?
541. In what way are iron and the year 1948 alike?
542. Who was created first, Adam or Eve?
543. Tell us the best way to make the hours go fast.
544. What is the best thing to take before singing?

545. Why should a cabman be brave?
546. Why is a Divinity student like a merchant?
547. Can you say how the lumberman invites a tree to fall?
548. What is the difference between a tight shoe and an oak tree?

549. Why is a watch like a river?
550. When is an old maid like a cigar?
551. Which is the favorite word with women?
552. What two letters of the alphabet contain nothing?
553. Why did Adam bite the apple Eve gave him?

554. What is the largest rope in the world?
555. Why is an island like the letter T?
556. What pins are used in soup?
557. Why is a bad picture like weak tea?
558. When can we say a student is very hungry?

559. What is black and white and red all over?
560. What word is always pronounced wrong?
561. How can you make five less by adding one to it?
562. What was it a blind man took at breakfast which restored his sight?

563. What is the best way to make a coat last?
564. Why is ivy climbing a tree like a watch?
565. Do you believe in clubs for the young folks?
566. What is a hot time?
567. What is it which *will be* yesterday and *was* tomorrow?

568. What is the difference between a barber and a sculptor?

569. Why is the letter E like London?

570. Why is Ireland like a bottle of wine?

571. When does a bather capture a large bird?

572. When is coffee like the soil?
573. How many peas in a pint?
574. When are houses like books?
575. Why is it right for B to come before C?
576. Why do you always put on your left shoe last?
577. Why are gloves unsalable articles?

578. When is an altered dress like a secret?

579. Why is a bootblack like the sun?

580. Why is a hungry man willing to be a martyr?

581. Of what trade is the sun?

582. How can you change a pumpkin into a squash?

583. Which burns longer, a wax or a tallow candle?
584. Why should a sailor be a good pugilist?
585. What is "Bred in Old Kentucky"?
586. How many sides has a circle?
587. What goes most against a farmer's grain?

588. Why is a circle of gold like the sound of a bell?
589. Why is a rifle a very insignificant weapon?
590. Who first introduced walking sticks?
591. When does a man weigh the most?
592. How is the best way to get fat?

593. Why does a cat wag its tail?
594. What is the best weather for making hay?
595. What is the favorite fruit of politicians?
596. Which is the merriest sauce?
597. What happens when there is an eclipse of the sun?
598. Why is the letter O like pain?

599. Why did Babe Ruth make so much money?

600. When is an express wagon like a forest?

601. When is a baby like a cup?

602. Why should we never write upon an empty stomach?

603. Where did Washington go when he was 39 years old?

604. Why is a kiss like gossip?

605. What bird looks most like a stork?

606. Why is the letter F like a fish-hook?

607. What nation does a criminal most dread?

608. What is a sure sign of a cold wave in March?

609. What is a calf after it is one year old?

610. Why was Adam's first day the longest?

611. What comes after butter?

612. Why is a good husband like dough?

613. Why is the Stock Exchange a den of wild beasts?

614. When does a ship fool you?
615. Why is early grass like a pen-knife?
616. What nation always wins in the end?
617. What is the best thing to take when one is run down?
618. Why is a nail fast in the wall like a sick old man?

619. What is hard to beat?
620. Why is a jailer like a pianist?
621. What age is served for break-fast?
622. Why do little birds in their nests agree?
623. Why is a good resolution like a fainting lady?
624. How do you swallow a door?

625. Why is the letter D like a wedding ring?
626. When does a son not take after his father?
627. On which side of the pitcher is the handle?
628. What are the most difficult ships to conquer?
629. What is the best book?

630. Why is a handsome woman like bread?

631. Why is a dirty child like flannel?

632. Why is the letter E like death?

633. What is a kiss?

634. Plant tight shoes and what will you raise?

635. When is money damp?

636. Who are they that feel most for their friends?

637. Why is sympathy like blind man's bluff?

638. Why are books your best friends?

639. What does x-p-d-n-c spell?

640. Why was Washington buried standing?

641. What four letters would frighten a thief?

642. Why are the Middle Ages called the Dark Ages?

643. How can the letter W be used to modernize music?

644. Why are laws like the ocean?

645. Why are soldiers usually in good company?

1001 RIDDLES FOR CHILDREN

646. If twelve make a dozen, how many make a million?
647. Which is proper to say, 5 plus 4 is 11, or are 11?
648. Why should soldiers be tired on the first of April?
649. Why should turtles be pitied?
650. Why are all duels very short affairs?

651. When does rain become too familiar with a lady?
652. Why is geology considered a deep science?
653. When does a man have to keep his word?
654. Why is a riddle like a parrot?
655. When are soldiers like good flannels?

656. Which is the proper newspaper for invalids?
657. What must you add to nine to make it six?

658. Why does a hen fly over the fence?
659. Why are washerwomen foolish?
660. Why does a dog bite his tail?
661. What game do the waves play at?
662. What has six feet and can sing?
663. Why is a defeated army like wool?
664. What pets make the sweetest music?
665. Why is the letter D like a sailor?

666. Why does a miller wear a white hat?
667. Why is the figure 9 like a peacock?
668. Why is a fish dealer never generous?
669. Why is a tired man like an umbrella?
670. What kind of hen lays the longest?
671. Where were the first doughnuts fried?
672. What is the best butter in the world?

673. What was Adam's favorite popular song?
674. What is the coldest place in a theatre?
675. Where did you go on your fifth birthday?
676. What fishes have eyes nearest together?
677. Why are weary people like automobiles?
678. What part of a fish weighs the most?
679. Which travels faster, heat or cold?
680. Where was Queen Elizabeth crowned?

681. Why should fish be well educated?
682. Why is a cherry like this book?
683. What part of speech is kissing?
684. When is a candle in a passion?
685. Why is a nobleman like a book?
686. When is a house like a crow?

687. Why is a hat like a king?
688. When is a pig like ink?
689. When are words musical?
690. What soap is the hardest?
691. How do you define a ring?
692. How much does a mule weigh?

693 What ring is most pleasant?

694. What bird is low-spirited?

695. Why are clouds like coach-men?

696. Why is a goose like an icicle?

697. Why are bookkeepers like hens?

698. What does a hen always do when she stands on one foot?

699. If you go into a cheese factory what smells the most?

700. Why is a muddy road a guardian of the public safety?

701. What is the difference between fog and a falling star?

702. What makes a pig the most unusual animal in the world?

703. What tree is of the greatest importance in history?

704. When is the time of the clock like the whistle of a train?

705. How many sticks go to the building of a raven's nest?

706. Name that bird which, if you do not, you will be sick.

707. Why is the letter D like a bad boy?

708. What shell fish are emblems of silence?

709. When does a man feel girlish?

710. What did Adam do when he wanted sugar?

711. Why are soldiers' guns always safe?

712. Why are lobsters like many politicians?

713. Why is it wrong to ship on board schooners?

714. Where is a good place to go when you're broke?

715. What has no head, nor arms, nor legs, and still has a tongue and a toe?

716. What does a person usually grow in a garden if he works hard?

717. When you look about you on a cold winter morning, what do you see on every hand?

718. What is the hardest thing about learning to ride a bicycle?

719. What goes all day, comes in at night, and stands with its tongue out?

720. Why does a man's hair generally turn gray sooner than his mustache?

721. What is the difference between 1941 and 1949 model automobiles?

722. How can you divide seventeen apples equally between eleven boys if four of them are very small?

723. Can you tell, to a quart, how much water flows through the Mississippi River in a day?

724. What is the difference between a sigh, a motor car, and a donkey?

725. Why does a baby boy always receive a hearty welcome in a family?

726. If you gave one friend fifteen cents and another a dime, what time would it be?

727. What is that which occurs twice in a moment, once in a minute, and not once in a thousand years?

728. What is the difference between a pitcher of water and a man throwing his wife into the river?

729. What is the difference between a young baby and a night cap?

730. What is the difference between a chimney-sweep and a man in a new suit of mourning?

731. Unable to think, unable to speak, yet tells the truth to all the world; what is it?

732. When a little boy gets his stockings on wrong side out, what does his mother do?

733. What birds have four feet and yellow feathers?

734. What is that which everyone wishes, yet wants to get rid of as soon as obtained?

735. When a shoemaker is about to make a shoe, what is the first thing he uses?

736. What is the difference between a skilled marksman and the man that tends the targets?

737. What is the difference between a horse who has been withdrawn from a race, and one who starts in a race and is beaten?

738. What relation is that child to its father who is not its father's own son?

739. Why did John's mother knit him three stockings when he was in the army?

740. Why is a list of celebrated musical composers like a saucepan?

741. What words may be pronounced quicker and shorter by adding syllables to them?

742. If a church is on fire, why has the organ the smallest chance of escape?

743. What is the difference between a tube and a foolish Dutchman?

744. If you saw a bird sitting on a twig and you wished to get the twig without disturbing the bird, what would you do?

745. What animal took the most luggage into the ark, and what animal took the least?

746. Why does a cat look first on one side and then on another when she enters a room?

747. What is the difference between a greyhound and a locomotive?

748. Which of your relatives are dependent upon you for a living?

749. What is the surest way to keep water from coming into your house?

750. Where was Adam going when he was in his thirty-ninth year?

751. What is it from which the whole may be taken, and yet some will remain?

752. What bird is it that is found in Africa, and although it has wings, it cannot fly?

753. What was the difference between Noah's ark and Joan of Arc?

754. Which is heavier, a pound of feathers or a pound of lead?

755. Why is a person who never makes a wager as bad as a regular gambler?

756. What is the difference between a minister and a chorus girl?

757. Why are different trees like different dogs?

758. In what way do men now compete with the birds?

759. What is that which divides by uniting, and unites by dividing?

760. When could the British Empire be purchased for the lowest sum?

761. How could the letter V make the calculations of a surveyor turn out wrong?

762. Why is snow easier to understand than any other sort of weather?

763. If the alphabet were going to a party, when would the last six letters start?

764. Name a carpenter's tool you can spell forward and backward the same way.

765. What is the difference between a well dressed man and a tired dog?

766. How can a man express himself and yet not speak one word?

767. What is the difference between a bright scholar and a bootblack?

768. Why is a man clearing a hedge at a single bound like one snoring?

769. What has two heads, one tail, four legs on one side, and two on the other?

770. When is a bald-headed man apt to be reminded of his youthful days?

771. If eight sparrows are on a roof and you shoot one, how many remain?

772. What is that which Adam never had, yet gave two to each of his children?

773. What is it that looks like a cat, eats like a cat, walks like a cat, yet is not a cat?

774. What is the difference between twice twenty-two and twice two and twenty?

775. Why is it easy to recall the famous pipe organ recital given in your town?

776. Why does the air seem fresher in winter than it does in summer?

777. What do we have in December that we do not have in any other month?

778. What is that which you can keep even after giving it to somebody else?

779. It never soars about the sky, yet often takes a fly; what is it?

780. Why is a very old umbrella that has been lost as good as new when found?

781. What is the difference between an engineer and a school teacher?

782. What is the difference between a man going upstairs and one looking up?

783. What part of a fish is like the end of a book?
784. Why is a man just imprisoned like a boat full of water?
785. What happens to a cat when it crosses a desert on Christmas Day?
786. What word is it which, by changing a single letter, becomes its own opposite?
787. Which is easier to spell,—fiddle - de - dee or fiddle - de dum?
788. Why does an American soldier wear brass buttons on his coat, and an Australian soldier wear steel ones?
789. Tom went out with his dog; he did not go before, behind, nor on one side of him, then where did he go?
790. When is a man greatly tickled but doesn't laugh?
791. What is that which every man can divide but which no man can see where it has been divided?
792. I came to town and met three people; they were neither men, nor women, nor children; what were they?
793. What is that which has never been felt, seen nor heard, never existed and still has a name?
794. In reading this book, where do you find a company, a veiled lady, and a noisy toy?
795. What is it that rises and falls, travels about and wears shoes out, but never had any shoes?

796. At what age is a man usually ready to get married?
797. What man must have his glass before he can do his day's work?
798. Why is a cigar-loving man like a tallow candle?
799. What is the difference between a farmer and a dress-maker?
800. What geometrical figure represents a lost parrot?
801. What magazine would be likely to give the best report of a fire?
802. What has neither wings nor a motor yet flies all over?
803. What is that which every one frequently holds yet rarely touches?
804. If a man gets up on a donkey, where should he get down?
805. Why is a son who objects to his mother's second marriage like an exhausted pedestrian?
806. Why are authors who treat of physiognomy like soldiers?
807. Why is a horse considered the most pessimistic of all animals?
808. How can it be proved that a horse has six legs?
809. If you place a baseball on the kitchen table, what is the first thing it will do?
810. What letter of the alphabet is needed to make a shoe?
811. Is there anything a man with a camera cannot take?
812. What word of only three syllables combines in it twenty-six letters?

813. What is the best way to keep fish from smelling?
814. Which is the only tool that grows sharper with use?
815. What is one of the largest words in the English language?
816. Why is a room full of married folks like an empty room?
817. Why should a horse not be hungry on a journey?
818. What letter will set one of the heavenly bodies in motion?
819. What instrument of war does an angry lover resemble?
820. What is the difference between a fisherman and a dunce?
821. If your neighbor quarreled with you and called you an insect, would he be wrong?
822. What is the difference between a soldier and a girl?
823. What is that which is often found where it is not?
824. Why does a pet dog wag his tail when he sees his master?
825. What did the big firecracker say to the little firecracker?
826. When is a black dog most likely to enter a house?

827. When is the only time a man is really immersed in his business?

828. What is that of which the common sort is the·best?

829. When does a man resemble an oak?

830. Why is a thief very comfortable?

831. What sentence did Adam use when he introduced himself to Eve, which reads the same backwards and forwards?

832. How do you make a slow horse fast?

833. When is an army totally destroyed?

834. What is the difference between a champion runner and a doctor's watch timing a pulse?

835. How can you shoot 120 hares at one shot?

836. What is a pig after it is three days old?

837. If all the money in the world were divided equally among the people what would each one get?

838. When is a newspaper like a delicate child?

839. What fish is most valued by a loving wife?

840. How many bushels of earth can you take out of a hole that is three feet square and three feet deep?

841. What men have made their mark in the world?

842. What is that which can play but can't walk?

843. What continent do you see when you look in the mirror in the morning?

844 What two numbers multiplied together make 7?

845. What sort of tie would a smart pig choose?

846. Why is your nose in the middle of your face?

847. Why is the history of England like a wet season?

848. Why is a poor singer like a counterfeiter?
849. How can you always have what you please?
850. When is a wall like a fish?
851. Why is a wise man like a pin?
852. When is a horse like a house?
853. When is a nation like a baby?
854. Which is the greatest riddle?
855. Why is a beggar like a baker?
856. What musical instrument should we never believe?
857. What three letters make a man of a boy?
858. Why is a talkative young man like a young pig?
859. How can you keep a dog from going mad in August?
860. Why is a pig in the parlor like a house on fire?
861. Which is the merriest letter in the alphabet?
862. Why is the food one eats on a rough sea voyage like a difficult riddle?
863. What is that which has neither flesh, bone or nail and yet has four fingers and a thumb?
864. Why is a man who is always complaining the easiest man to satisfy?
865. What are the best trees to protect a house from winter storms?

866. Why is the letter B like fire?
867. Why are balloons like beggars?
868. What men are most above board?
869. What makes the ocean get angry?
870. Who sits before the Queen with his hat on?

871. What insect is found in school?
872. What letters are most provoking?
873. Why does a wife hug her husband?
874. What flies up but still is down?
875. Why is a dog's tail like the heart of a tree?

876. What are the embers of a year soon to close?
877. Why is the inside of everything mysterious?
878. What is the difference between the milky way, and a room full of great-grandfathers?
879. Why is a lollipop like a horse?

880. What makes more noise than a pig in a sty?

881. Why are your nose and chin always at odds?

882. What is the difference between a chicken who is sickly and seven days?

883. What animal keeps the best time?

884. When a boy falls into the water, what is the first thing he does?

885. What is the best way to grow fat?

886. What is the most moral musical instrument?

887. When is a girl not sorry to lose her hair?

888. What is the hardest thing to deal with?

889. What wind would a hungry sailor prefer?

890. What does the garden say when it laughs?

891. If you were riding on a jackass what fruit would you resemble?

892. What ship has two mates but no captain?
893. Why is the letter K like a pig's tail?
894. What nation produces the most marriages?
895. What is it that runs in and out of town all day and night?

896. What is the difference between one yard and two yards?
897. Why do girls kiss each other, but men do not?
898. When is it no misfortune for a young lady to lose her good name?
899. What coat is finished without buttons and put on wet?

900. Why should ladies who wish to remain slender avoid the letter C?
901. What is the difference between a lover and his rival?
902. Why was the elephant the last animal in the ark?
903. Why is the palate of the mouth like a dejected man?

904. What is that which is invisible yet never out of sight?

905. What is the difference between a tunnel and an ear-trumpet?

906. What well-known band never plays popular music?

907. Why do children object to the absence of Santa Claus?

908. What part of speech are shopkeepers most anxious to dispose of?

909. How do we know they had fruit on board the ark?

910. In what sort of syllables ought a parrot to speak?

911. What is the difference between the sun and bread?

912. What was the greatest feat of strength ever performed?

913. If two's company, and three's a crowd, what are four and five?

914. What is the difference between the earth and the sea?

915. Why is a teacher of music necessarily a good teacher?

916. When does a farmer act with great rudeness to his grain?
917. What state is round at both ends, and high in the middle?
918. What part of a locomotive requires the most attention?
919. What is the difference between a cat and a comma?
920. Why should a man never tell his secrets in a cornfield?
921. What kind of cat do you always find in a library?
922. What is that which, by losing an "I", has nothing left but a nose?
923. What is the best way to carry water in a sieve?
924. Why is a star in the heavens like a window in the roof?

925. What food is an unknown quantity?
926. Why can't we fight with actresses?
927. Why is a herring like a graveyard?
928. What are the biggest kind of ants?
929. Why is a policeman like a rainbow?
930. What insect does a blacksmith make?
931. How do bees dispose of their honey?
932. Why is a windy orator like a whale?
933. When is a rope like a stick of wood?

934. Why does a warm day give an icicle a bad reputation?
935. What is the color of grass when covered with snow?
936. What kind of robbery may be said to be not dangerous?
937. How can you keep postage stamps from sticking together?

938. What is the difference between an auction and seasickness?
939. What does a housekeeper look for, yet hate to find?
940. When is it socially correct to serve milk in a saucer?
941. If Jack's father is Joe's son, what relation is Jack to Joe?
942. Who are the two largest ladies in the United States?

943. What should a minister preach about?
944. What has a white gown and a red cap?
945. Why is a wedding ring like eternity?
946. Why is a coward like a leaky barrel?
947. What is smaller than an ant's mouth?
948. What is the best material for kites?
949. Who is the oldest lunatic on record?
950. Which are the most sensible letters?

951. When should any pig be able to write?
952. What are the two strangest happenings?
953. What is a pig doing when he is eating?
954. Why is a fool in a high station like a man in a balloon?
955. What would you call a man who is always wiring for money?
956. Why are chickens economical things for a farmer to keep?
957. Can you spell donkey with one letter that has no curve?
958. Why does the Statue of Liberty stand in New York Harbor?
959. What were the colors of the wind and waves in a storm?
960. Why does a chicken cross over the street in the mud?
961. What did Jack Frost say when he kissed the violet?
962. Why is a leaf of a tree like the human body?
963. How does a sailor know there is a man in the moon?
964. How can you keep a rooster from crowing on Sunday?
965. When water becomes ice, what great change occurs?
966. What's more wonderful than a dog that can count?
967. What can pass before the sun without making a shadow?
968. Why would a compliment from a chicken be an insult?
969. When are potatoes used for mending clothes?
970. Why is a sculptor's death the most terrible?
971. Why is a pair of stockings like a very old person?
972. How does a postage stamp differ from a boy?

973. When are you not yourself?
974. When did the fly fly?
975. What does the evening wear?
976. Where does the captain of a ship keep his hens?

977. What dance do bakers prefer?
978. What man always finds things dull?
979. Why is snow different from Sunday?
980. "Railroad Crossing, Look out for the cars"; Can you spell it without any r's?
981. Two Indians standing on a bridge, one is the father of the other one's son. What relation are the two Indians?
982. Whose best works are most trampled on?
983. If a boy saw his sister fall into a well, why could he not rescue her?
984. If I had an apple and you had only a bite, what would you do?
985. What is the name of the feathers that grow on a chicken's wing?
986. What makes everyone sick except those who swallow it?
987. What letter in the Dutch alphabet will name a titled lady?
988. If a Uneeda biscuit is a soda cracker, what is an ice-pick?

989. Why does a white horse never pay toll?
990. How can a poor man be equal to a millionaire in station?
991. Why are the days long in summer and short in winter?
992. What is most like a horse's foot?
993. What is the most disagreeable month to a soldier?
994. Why is your shadow like a false friend?
995. Add ten to nothing and what animal does it make?
996. What is the gentlest kind of spur?
997. If a boy wears his pants out, what will he do?
998. Why is it impossible to sweep out a room?
999. Why is a good resolution like a looking glass?
1000. What are the most unsociable things in the world?
1001. Why is the emblem of the United States more enduring than that of France, England, Ireland, or Scotland?

ANSWERS FOR 1001 RIDDLES

1. Two calves.
2. When he is a-bed.
3. Four; calling a tail a leg doesn't make it one.
4. White, because there are more of them.
5. A little girl.
6. When he can't help it.
7. None. They are all outside.
8. They must be strapped.
9. One you lick with a stick the other you stick with a lick.
10. The barber.
11. Because they are all tail-bearers.
12. When it is felt.
13. George Washington, the father of his country.
14. "Are you asleep?"
15. Time to get it fixed.
16. When it reaches the bottom.
17. The letter Y.
18. The bridge of your nose.
19. Pharoah's daughter. She drew a profit (prophet) from a rush on the bank.
20. A pillow.
21. February because it is the shortest.
22. Because we cannot see through it.
23. Plenty of hair.
24. It has nails.
25. When it rains cats and dogs.
26. One, after which his stomach was not empty.
27. Long enough to reach the ground.
28. They wear their hair longer.
29. A bedstead.
30. Carpet.
31. A run in her stocking.
32. An umbrella.
33. It saw the apple turn over.
34. A falsehood.
35. Turkey.
36. Because it would then be a foot.
37. It makes him yell "Oh" (yellow).
38. When rattled.
39. False teeth.
40. Where the son (sun) sets.
41. Because you cannot get them for nothing.
42. None. You have to put them in the pot.
43. The letter b.
44. When they beat the eggs and whip the cream.
45. Lock from a bald head.
46. A shadow.
47. In Noah's Ark.
48. Two shoes.
49. Both need beating.
50. With a spoon.
51. Storyland.
52. Because he is always pursuing his studies.
53. One, if it was long enough.
54. The letter "g".
55. It never shows a white feather.
56. When it catches a mouse.
57. Maid of Orleans.
58. When you are Chili (chilly).
59. A half moon, because the full moon is lighter.
60. As far as the center and then you will be going out.
61. Twice as long as half its length.
62. Cool.
63. Because she has a head on one side and a tail on the other.
64. Samson. He brought down the house.
65. Because the sun sets on them every night.
66. Yew (you).
67. The barber.
68. A sponge.
69. Christmas of course.
70. It takes two to make it.
71. Advice.
72. Silence.
73. When he is a greyhound.
74. Lie still.
75. Because he is an ass.
76. A donkey.
77. When he slept with his forefathers.
78. When she has a comb in her hair.
79. Your name.
80. The elder.
81. Dead men.
82. Your age.
83. Tulips.
84. A garbage wagon.
85. Infant.
86. When it is a bad one.
87. Your portrait.
88. When he is a little hoarse.
89. Mocking bird.
90. By pulling its tail.
91. Its spots.
92. A road.
93. Snow.
94. A pig pen.
95. When he is short of money.
96. The whale that brought him up.
97. Both have to be licked.
98. A baseball team.
99. On the outside, of course.
100. A hole.

101. A ditch.
102. Tulips.
103. When bare-footed.
104. A conflagration.
105. He felt down in the mouth.
106. A dandelion and a tiger-lily.
107. When it strikes one.
108. Because it is hard to fill.
109. The beggar was a woman.
110. Because it leaves in the early spring.
111. When it is made into a ruler.
112. Lift the hood and look in.
113. A needle.
114. An elephant can have fleas but a flea can't have elephants.
115. A mushroom.
116. A cord of wood.
117. A screw driver.
118. It is a "dear little thing."
119. Joseph because Pharaoh made a ruler out of him.
120. Postage.
121. A whetstone (wet stone).
122. When it is a-light.
123. It wasn't raining.
124. A goat.
125. Because it goes against his stomach.
126. When she is dressed to kill.
127. Because it contains many currents.
128. When it is made into little pats.
129. When it is a chop-house.
130. Because it must be ground before it is used.
131. A date.
132. A coat that is not paid for.
133. Fortune.
134. In your pocket.
135. The car-fare.
136. Ten cents.
137. One without whiskers.
138. His salary.
139. When flowing.
140. Because it beats time.
141. Because you always stop looking when you find it.
142. One is a hunted stag and the other a stunted hag.
143. The paper one because when you put it in your pocket you double it, and when you take it out again you see it in creases.
144. Water.
145. Because they are too dear (two deer).
146. Because it's light when it rises.
147. Because they have eyes to see what they are doing.
148. One longs to eat and the other eats too long.
149. When it is a-jar.
150. Your mother.
151. Because they can't chew.
152. Because he is full of pains (panes).
153. A doorbell.
154. When it is dripping.
155. Mis-fortune.

156. When there are two of them.
157. When it makes a spring.
158. Because Noah sat on the deck.
159. Because it's a false hood.
160. Against his will.
161. A smile.
162. The letter L.
163. When you are popping it.
164. It saw the salad dressing.
165. The horse.
166. The roof of the mouth.
167. The paper on the wall.
168. The rent.
169. Hannah.
170. What does y-e-s spell?
171. Because there is never any change in it.
172. The side which is not eaten.
173. When there are two beats (beets) to the measure.
174. Because he is accustomed to see (sea) sickness.
175. The dentist.
176. A doctor.
177. Because it is catching.
178. A mirror.
179. Because they are only slightly connected.
180. Sun-beams.
181. A player piano.
182. One is "hard-up" and the other is soft down.
183. The library has the most stories.
184. Because it will change ice into mice.
185. Five cents.
186. When it is re-covered.
187. Otherwise it would be a foot.
188. Every watch has a spring.
189. Yesterday.
190. Because they live by hook or by crook.
191. A pump handle.
192. It goes out.
193. She couldn't stir.
194. Merely a difference of time—one has feeling and the other has felt.
195. By going from one spot to another.
196. The widow's mite and the wicked flee.
197. A comb.
198. Hand-cuffs.
199. A little above two feet.
200. Ashes.
201. War-fare.
202. An umbrella.
203. When it is sat-in.
204. The multiplication table.
205. When you are in bed.
206. The roof of the mouth.
207. Because she is something to a door (adore).
208. A pack of cards.
209. When it can't bear you.
210. Air castles.
211 Because it is the center of light.
212. A half-dollar.

213. Because the worse people are the more they are with them.
214. A window-pane.
215. When he is in a pickle.
216. The back of a clock.
217. A single spring.
218. Because it begins by breaking.
219. Because they never saw it.
220. When he turns his horse to grass and also when he turns his cow to pasture.
221. When his designs are bad.
222. Because without it she would be a "young lad."
223. Job. He had more patience (patients) than any man.
224. It is under the lash.
225. Engineers.
226. A river.
227. Stoves.
228. Your feet from the floor.
229. Because he always brings his trunk.
230. The letter F.
231. The one you wear, the other you were.
232. When it has a hole in it.
233. Cain when he hit A-bel.
234. The price of admission.
235. When the cow jumped over the moon.
236. Two and one to carry.
237. Room for improvement.
238. A step farther (step-father).
239. Put the fire out.
240. An old TEN dollar rather than a new ONE.
241. If he knows his business he can always draw money.
242. Because he is crusty.
243. When it is grated.
244. Becauue of the sand which is (sandwiches) there.
245. To Hungary.
246. Mice.
247. Because if you don't C sharp you will B flat.
248. In the dictionary.
249. They are continually "crossing the line" and going from pole to pole.
250. As Mr. So-and-So (sew and sew).
251. To keep a check on his stomach.
252. When it is put out.
253. A bee (b) will follow it.
254. One goes quick on her legs; the other goes quack on her legs.
255. When it's under canvas.
256. When it's adrift.
257. Marriage (Marri-age).
258. When she is a little dear (deer).
259. Because he makes pa pay.
260. A fair-haired girl.
261. David because he rocked Goliath to sleep.
262. When you double your fists.
263. Potatoes.
264. Because they play most of the time.
265. An American boy.
266. Because a friend in need is a friend indeed.
267. When taught (taut).
268. When he takes a roll in bed.
269. A time-table.
270. Because they lie too long in them.
271. Spending your last dollar on a purse.
272. Because a needle is no good without an eye.
273. Fold it.
274. Absence of body.
275. When deprived of its arms.
276. When they begin to knit.
277. A draft.
278. Time.
279. It hasn't the face to do it.
280. It must be broken before it can be used.
281. On the side of his head.
282. When it begins to root.
283. The mistletoe.
284. Because his tale (tail) grows out of his head.
285. Because both make the ear-ring.
286. When he takes the floor.
287. When he gives them fits.
288. One is female, the other is mail-fee.
289. Because it always advances with a bow.
290. Mis-take.
291. When it is crossed.
292. Nothing.
293. Your teeth.
294. One is sworn in and the other is worn out.
295. The nose.
296. Because it's round.
297. Cape Farewell.
298. To keep his wig warm (wigwam).
299. When there is a leek (leak) in it.
300. The letter T.
301. In the dictionary.
302. Daylight.
303. Glass.
304. A quartet.
305. For dentistry because they have a good pull.
306. When he is out of patients.
307. Because he does not feel well.
308. A barber has razors to shave and a mother has shavers to raise.
309. Five after one.
310. When it runs down and strikes.
311. Because it suits (soots) everyone who tries it.
312. When it is cutting.
313. For-bidding.
314. Because it is knot.
315. Because it has no point.
316. When Noah brought Ham into the ark.
317. When the wind makes them water.
318. Because she had sufficient ground for remaining.
319. Yes, Mississippi.
320. Your hair.
321. To hold up his pants.
322. When he has a pain (pane) in his stomach.

323. The one with the largest head.
324. The railroad tracks.
325. The other half.
326. When it is a crab.
327. Australia was always the largest.
328. Because it has a Marblehead.
329. Elliptical (a lip tickle).
330. The letter N.
331. By the Sound.
332. F O E.
333. When autumn turns the leaves.
334. Your own nose.
335. His foot.
336. She weighs anchor.
337. The last person takes the plate with the cookie.
338. One sells watches and the other watches cells.
339. A watch.
340. A dandelion (dandy lion).
341. The match.
342. Because it's a long time before they leave.
343. A woman crossing a bridge with a pail of water on her head.
344. A bald head.
345. The moon.
346. His left elbow.
347. He might get a quarterback.
348. Because they carry a monkey around in the streets.
349. Because they both go to the head.
350. All the difference in the world.
351. Because you can't take a nickel from a copper.
352. When she is on fire.
353. The baby is a little bigger.
354. Because it never appears in good spirits.
355. Sunday. The rest are week days.
356. Because it comes from a blow.
357. A pair of long legs.
358. A clock.
359. Stop a minute.
360. Because he is true to the last.
361. One knows his stops and the other stops his nose.
362. Grass is.
363. Because they are warranted to wash and keep their color.
364. Because they grow bigger by nursing.
365. Because it never does write (right) by itself.
366. As long as he was Abel.
367. One is to be well shaken before taking and the other is to be taken and then shaken.
368. Because the bed will not come to us.
369. Make them.
370. Toll gates.
371. The nails in your shoes.
372. Toothpicks.
373. Ivy (IV).
374. When she has a toothache.
375. Music.
376. Not if the clock strikes first.
377. Butter.
378. Because it works both ways.
379. A Sharp Major.
380. When it is (s) ticking there.
381. Because it is planted in the spring.
382. Just a little before Eve.
383. A brick-bat.
384. The shortest day.
385. Both are far-fetched.
386. Vacci-nation, because it is always in arms.
387. Lack of hair.
388. The stone would get wet.
389. A leek (leak).
390. Ur-chins.
391. Because it represents hard-ware (wear).
392. When they won't go over the inn-step.
393. Tre-mend-us!
394. A keyhole.
395. The Canary Islands.
396. The 12:50 because it's ten to one if you catch it.
397. Because it is always running down its own works.
398. Lawyers.
399. To let you through.
400. The lead weighs a pound the pianist pounds away.
401. Growing older.
402. Because it is made up of rounds.
403. A lawsuit.
404. They are in a "mess" every day at sea.
405. On the head.
406. The crane.
407. Roots.
408. A yardstick.
409. The Sandwich Islands.
410. Dates.
411. Lapland.
412. The road.
413. One sews seams nice and the other seems so nice.
414. The figure 6.
415. The morning glory.
416. A quack doctor.
417. It has many pages.
418. Make her fast.
419. A feather.
420. Riding in an airplane.
421. For fear of falling out.
422. Because peel follows peel in an onion, and peal follows peal in a ringing bell.
423. A cat lights on its feet and a match on its head.
424. Because it is too far to walk.
425. Buy both in New York and send them to Maine.
426. Because it doesn't know how to conduct itself.
427. Because its success depends on the batter.
428. When it is smoked.
429. Because it can't be beat (beet).
430. G-O-A-T.
431. Mustard.
432. It takes leaven ('leven) to make a loaf.
433. Jelly beans.

434. Cork.
435. The last.
436. In the days of No-a before U and I were born.
437. Four quarters.
438. A policeman.
439. All the difference in the world.
440. The butcher.
441. When it's bunged up.
442. Because he is discharged.
443. Because they are good at drawing houses.
444. Because he carries his calves there.
445. When he presses his suit.
446. One is lowered to take passengers up, and the other is highered (hired) to do it.
447. A comb.
448. Hailing street cars.
449. A river.
450. "Whoa!"
451. Because she can't lay a brick.
452. The letter B.
453. Patricks.
454. Because though always first in pity he is always last in help.
455. Because they are often drilled.
456. The outside.
457. Because there is always a night in between.
458. Because it begins with a squall.
459. The letter B.
460. Because it is composed of rags.
461. An outdoor ice-skating rink.
462. Thanks.
463. A noise.
464. Because they are naturally well red (read).
465. Because he is let out at night, and taken in in the morning.
466. When it's read (red) of course.
467. An echo.
468. In the days of Noah (No A).
469. A typesetter.
470. Because it will be long enough before he gets another.
471. Yes; one skims the milk the other the water.
472. In grinding scissors.
473. Thirty-seven years; how do I now? He told me his age.
474. A perch in a bird's cage.
475. They belong to a standing army.
476. Mrs. Hobson.
477. Because they occasionally go out at night when they should not.
478. When he discovers a new "star."
479. When it's on the train.
480. Tissue ('tis you).
481. A clock.
482. It runs.
483. Why simply take one candle out of the box, and the box will be a candle lighter.
484. Because he is one beside himself.
485. The noise.
486. One gets all the honey the other all the wax (whacks).
487. Because they both lose their bark when they die.
488. It will give us many good points.
489. The road hog.
490. Because they take away a peck at a time.
491. It is match less.
492. People plant them and they shoot.
493. Porcupine.
494. The Inn-experienced.
495. On a baseball field!
496. When it becomes a little bolder (boulder).
497. The future.
498. Because they both have to do with the fall of man.
499. By listening to the tree bark.
500. An open-faced watch.
501. He is likely to reign (rain).
502. Smoke.
503. To pull his wagon.
504. Because he would get six times as much money.
505. Go to church late.
506. Because one makes a din, and the other a dinner.
507. One lays at pleasure; the other plays at leisure.
508. Because he is dead.
509. Ink.
510. One plays for his pay and the other pays for his play.
511. Because you are passing counterfeit money.
512. Eight.
513. She weighs candy.
514. One harms the cheese, the other charms the he's.
515. Because it is breaking through the sealing (ceiling).
516. The postman.
517. Yes with an egg-beater.
518. Let it rain.
519. Neither one, a horse can't sing.
520. Because they are long enough.
521. Because it is high bread (bred).
522. A shoe.
523. A secret.
524. Because they are murmurs of the tied (tide).
525. A stocking.
526. Get water from the springs and dates from the calendar.
527. When Joseph served in Pharaoh's Court.
528. Because one good turn deserves another.
529. In a lifetime.
530. Because without it we would have neither Christmas nor New Year.
531. Because it comes in the middle of day.
532. A cabinet-maker.
533. An heir-loom.
534. The roof.
535. A goose has many quills, but an author can make a goose of himself with one quill.
536. Stone (St) one.
537. Because he possesses a good constitution.

538. It is out of the head.
539. B Natural.
540. Because so many people are trying to kill it.
541. Both are ore (o'er).
542. Eve was, for she was the first maid (made).
543. Use the spur of the moment.
544. Breath.
545. Because none but the brave deserve the fair (fare).
546. Because he studies the prophets (profits).
547. He "axes" it.
548. One makes corns ache, the other makes acorns.
549. Because it won't run long without winding.
550. When you have no match for it.
551. The last one.
552. M.T. (empty).
553. Because he had no knife to cut it.
554. Europe.
555. Because it is in the midst of water.
556. Terrapins.
557. Because it is not well drawn.
558. When he "devours" books.
559. A newspaper.
560. Wrong.
561. IV.
562. He took a cup and—saw sir (saucer).
563. By making the trousers and vest first.
564. Because it is a stem-winder.
565. Only when kindness fails.
566. A clock in an oven.
567. Why today, of course!
568. One curls up and dyes; the other makes faces and busts.
569. Because it is the capital of England.
570. Because it has a Cork in it.
571. When he takes a duck in the water.
572. When it is ground.
573. One P.
574. When they have stories.
575. Because we must B before we can C.
576. When you have put on one the other is left.
577. Because they are made to be kept on hand.
578. When it is let out.
579. Because they shine all day.
580. Because he is ready to go to the stake (steak).
581. A tanner.
582. Throw it up and it will come down a-squash.
583. Neither, both burn shorter.
584. Because he is always boxing the compass.
585. Fifteen cents a loaf.
586. Two. Outside and inside.
587. The reaping machine.
588. It is a ring.
589. Because it is within a "t" of being trifle.
590. Eve, when she presented Adam with a little Cain.
591. When he is heaviest.
592. Go to the butcher shop.
593. Because it wants to.
594. When it rains pitchforks.

595. Plums.
596. Caper sauce.
597. A great many people come out to look at it.
598. Because it makes man, moan.
599. Because a good batter makes good dough.
600. When it is full of trunks.
601. When it is a tea thing (teething).
602. Paper is preferable.
603. Into his 40th year.
604. Because it goes from mouth to mouth.
605. The stork's wife.
606. Because it will make eel feel.
607. Condem-nation.
608. The thermometer.
609. Two years old.
610. Because it had no Eve.
611. Cheese.
612. Because a woman needs (kneads) him.
613. The members are bulls and bears.
614. When it lies at the wharf.
615. Because the spring brings out the blades.
616. Determi-nation.
617. The number of the car.
618. Because it is in firm.
619. A drum with a hole in it.
620. Because he fingers the keys.
621. Sausage.
622. Because they are afraid of falling out.
623. Because it ought to be carried out.
624. Bolt it.
625. You could not have wed without it.
626. When his father leaves him nothing to take.
627. The outside.
628. Hard-ships.
629. A pocketbook.
630. Because she is often toasted.
631. Because it shrinks from washing.
632. It is the end of life.
633. Nothing, divided by two.
634. Corns.
635. When it is due in the morning and mist at night.
636. The blind.
637. Because it is a fellow feeling for a fellow creature.
638. Because, when they bore you, you can shut them up without giving offense.
639. Expediency.
640. Because he couldn't lie.
641. O I C U.
642. Because there were so many nights (knights) then.
643. By changing SING TO SWING.
644. Because the most trouble is caused by the breakers.
645. They are generally associated with big guns.
646. Very few.
647. Neither; 5 plus 4 are 9.
648. Because they have just had a march of thirty-one days.
649. Because theirs is a hard case.

650. Because it only requires two seconds to arrange them.
651. When it begins to pat her (patter) on the back.
652. Because it penetrates into the earth.
653. When no one will take it.
654. It is far-fetched and full of nonsense.
655. When they don't shrink.
656. The weekly (weakly) news.
657. S, for IX with S is six.
658. Because she cannot go around it.
659. Because they set tubs to catch soft water when it rains hard.
660. To make both ends meet.
661. At pitch and toss.
662. A trio.
663. Because it is worsted.
664. Trumpets.
665. It follows the C (sea).
666. To cover his head.
667. Because without a tail it is nothing.
668. Because his business makes him sell fish (selfish).
669. Because he is used up.
670. A dead one.
671. In Greece (grease).
672. The goat.
673. "There's Only One Girl in This World for Me."
674. Z Row (Zero).
675. Into your sixth year.
676. The smallest.
677. Because they are always tired.
678. Its scales.
679. Heat. You catch cold.
680. On the head.
681. They are found in schools.
682. Because it is red (read).
683. A conjunction.
684. When it is put out or when it flares up.
685. Because he has a title.
686. When it has wings.
687. It has a crown.
688. When you put it in a pen.
689. When they have a ring to them.
690. Cast steel (Castile)
691. As a hole with a rim around it.
692. Get on the scales and see.
693. The ring for dinner.
694. The blue bird.
695. Because they hold the reins (rains).
696. Because they both grow down.
697. Because they have to scratch for a living.
698. She holds up the other.
699. Your nose.
700. Because it reduces the speed of autos.
701. One is mist on earth, the other is missed in heaven.
702. Because you first kill him and then cure him.
703. The date.
704. When it is two to two.
705. None. They are all carried.
706. Swallow.
707. Because it makes ma mad.
708. Oysters.
709. When he makes his maiden speech.
710. Raised Cain.
711. Because every one of them has a lock.
712. Because they change color when they get into hot water.
713. Because no man should serve two-masters.
714. Go to work.
715. A shoe.
716. Tired.
717. A glove.
718. The pavement.
719. A wagon.
720. Because it is about twenty-one years older.
721. Eight years.
722. By making them into apple sauce.
723. Yes, two pints.
724. A sigh is, Oh dear, a motor car is too dear, a donkey is you dear.
725. Because it never comes a-miss.
726. A quarter to two.
727. The letter M.
728. One is water in the pitcher, and the other is pitch her in the water.
729. One is born to wed, and the other is worn to bed.
730. One is blacked with soot, and the other suited with black.
731. A perfect pair of scales.
732. Turns the hose on him.
733. Two canaries.
734. A good appetite.
735. The last.
736. One hits the mark, and the other marks the hit.
737. One fails to start, and the other starts to fail.
738. His daughter.
739. Because John wrote her that he had gotten so tall he had grown another foot.
740. Because it would be incomplete without a Handel.
741. Quick and short.
742. Because the engine cannot play upon it.
743. One is a hollow cylinder and the other a silly Hollander.
744. Wait till he flew off.
745. The elephant took his trunk; and the fox had only a brush.
746. Because it can't look on both sides at the same time.
747. One is trained to run and the other runs a train.
748. Your uncles, aunts and cousins, for without U they could not exist.
749. Don't pay your water tax.
750. Into his fortieth.
751. The word "Wholesome".
752. A dead one.
753. One was made of wood and the other was Maid of Orleans.

754. Each weigh one pound.
755. Because he is no bettor.
756. The minister says "Amen," and the chorus girl says "Ah men!"
757. Because each has a different bark.
758. In flying through the air.
759. Scissors.
760. When Richard the Third offered his kingdom for a horse.
761. Because it turns an ALLEY into a VALLEY.
762. Because it is the only one of which you can see the drift.
763. After T.
764. Level.
765. The man wears an entire suit while the tired dog just pants.
766. When he takes an express train.
767. One shines at the head, the other at the foot.
768. Because he does it in his leap (his sleep).
769. A lady on horse-back riding side saddle.
770. When he thinks of his top.
771. One. The one you shot.
772. Parents.
773. A kitten.
774. One is 44, and the other 24.
775. Because it was the night of the big wind.
776. Because its kept on ice most of the time.
777. The letter D.
778. Your word.
779. A spider.
780. Because it's re-covered.
781. One minds the train, and the other trains the mind.
782. One is stepping up stairs and the other is staring up steps.
783. The finis.
784. Because he requires bailing out.
785. It gets sandy claws (Santa Claus).
786. United, untied.
787. The former, because it is spelled with more e's (ease).
788. To keep his coat buttoned.
789. On the other side.
790. When a fly lights upon his nose.
791. Water.
792. A man, a woman, and a child.
793. Nothing.
794. Reading this co-nun-drum.
795. A football.
796. At the parsonage.
797. A glazier.
798. Because he will smoke when he is going out.
799. One gathers what he sows; the other sews what she gathers.
800. A polygon (polly gone).
801. A powder magazine.
802. A used piece of fly paper.
803. His tongue.
804. From a swan's breast.

805. Because he can't go a step farther (stepfather).
806. Because they write (right) about face.
807. Because he always neighs (nays).
808. He has fore (four) legs in front and two behind.
809. It looks 'round.
810. The last.
811. Yes, a hint.
812. Alphabet.
813. Cut their noses off.
814. The tongue.
815. Smiles, because there is a mile between the first and last letters.
816. Because there is not a single person in it.
817. Because he always has a bit in his mouth.
818. T, because it will make a star start.
819. A cross bow (beau).
820. One baits his hook and the other hates his book.
821. Yes, an insect has six legs.
822. One faces the powder and the other powders the face.
823. Fault.
824. Because he has one to wag.
825. "My pop's bigger than your pop!"
826. When the door is open.
827. When he is giving a swimming lesson.
828. Sense.
829. When growing a-corn.
830. Because he takes things easy.
831. "Madam, I'm Adam!"
832. When you stop feeding him.
833. When the soldiers are all in quarters.
834. One beats the record and the other records the beats.
835. Fire at a wig.
836. Four days old.
837. An equal share.
838. When it appears weekly.
839. Her-ring.
840. None. It has been taken out.
841. Those who can't write.
842. A piano.
843. You see Europe (you're up).
844. Seven times one.
845. A pig sty (pig's tie).
846. It is the scenter (center).
847. Because it is full of reigns (rains).
848. Because he is an utterer of bad notes.
849. Be pleased with what you have.
850. When it is scaled.
851. Because he has a head and comes to a point.
852. When he has blinds on.
853. When it is in arms.
854. Life, because we all have to give it up.
855. Because he needs (kneads).
856. A lyre.
857. A-G-E.
858. Because he is likely to become a great bore (boar).

859. Shoot him in July.
860. The sooner it's put out the better.
861. U, because it is always in fun.
862. Because one is obliged to give it up.
863. A glove.
864. Because nothing satisfies him.
865. Fur trees (fir trees).
866. Because it makes oil boil.
867. Because they have no visible means of support.
868. Chessmen.
869. It has been crossed so often.
870. The coachman.
871. The spelling bee.
872. The T's (tease).
873. Because she wants to get around him.
874. A feather.
875. Because it's farthest from the bark.
876. Nov-ember and Dec-ember.
877. Because we can't make it out.
878. One is a lot of old stars, the other a lot of old pa's.
879. Because the more you lick it the faster it goes.
880. Two pigs.
881. Because words are constantly passing between them.
882. One is a weak one. and the other is one week.
883. The watch dog.
884. He gets wet.
885. Raise pigs.
886. An upright piano.
887. When she has it bobbed.
888. An old pack of cards.
889. One that blows foul (fowl) and chops about.
890. "Hoe, hoe, hoe!"
891. A pear (pair).
892. Courtship.
893. Because it is at the end of pork.
894. Fascination.
895. A road.
896. A fence.
897. Because girls have nothing better to kiss and men have.
898. When a young man gives a better one.
899. A coat of paint.
900. Because it makes FAT a FACT.
901. One kisses the miss, and the other misses the kiss.
902. Because he stayed behind to pack his trunk.
903. Because they are both down in the mouth.
904. The letter i.
905. One is hollowed out and the other is hollered in.
906. A hat band.
907. Because they prefer his presence (presents).
908. Articles.
909. Because the animals went in pairs (pears).
910. In poly-syllables.
911. The sun rises in the east and the bread rises with the y-east in it.
912. Wheeling, West Virginia.
913. Nine.

914. One is dirty, the other tidy.
915. Because she is a sound instructor.
916. When he pulls its ears and threshes it.
917. OHIO.
918. The "tender" part.
919. The cat has claws at the end of his paws; the comma is a pause at the end of a clause.
920. Because there are so many ears there and they would be shocked.
921. A catalogue.
922. A no(i)se.
923. Freeze the water first.
924. Because it is a sky-light.
925. Hash.
926. They make up too quickly.
927. Because it is full of bones.
928. Gi-ants.
929. Because he rarely appears until the storm is over.
930. The Fire-fly.
931. They cell it.
932. Because he often rises to spout.
933. When it has knots.
934. Because it becomes an eavesdropper.
935. Invisible green.
936. A safe robbery.
937. Buy one at a time.
938. One is a sale of effects and the other is the effects of a sail.
939. Dust.
940. When you feed a cat.
941. Joe is his grandfather.
942. Miss Ouri and Mrs. Sippi (Missouri and Mississippi).
943. About half an hour.
944. A candle.
945. Because it has no beginning and no end.
946. They both run.
947. What goes into it.
948. Fly paper.
949. Time out of mind.
950. The wise (Y's).
951. When he is turned into a pen.
952. A deaf and dumb man picked up a wheel and spoke, a blind man picked up a hammer and saw.
953. Making a hog of himself.
954. Because he appears little to everybody and everybody appears little to the balloonist.
955. An electrician.
956. Because for every grain they give a peck.
957. I.
958. Because it can't sit down.
959. The wind blue (blew)—the waves rose.
960. To get on the other side.
961. Wilt thou? And it wilted.
962. Because it has veins in it.
963. Because he went to see (sea).

964. Get him stuffed on Saturday night.
965. A change in pr-ice.
966. A spelling bee.
967. The wind.
968. Because it would be fowl (foul) language.
969. When they are put in patches.
970. Because he makes faces and "busts."
971. Because they are on their last legs.
972. It can only be licked once.
973. When you are a little pale (pail).
974. When the spider spider (spied her).
975. The close (clothes) of day.
976. In the hatchway.
977. A-bun-dance.
978. A scissors grinder.
979. Because it can fall on any day in the week.
980. I-t.
981. Husband and wife.
982. A shoemaker, because good shoes last longer than bad ones.
983. Because he could not be a brother and assist her (a sister) too.
984. Scratch it.

985. Chicken feathers.
986. Flattery.
987. Dutch-S.
988. A water cracker.
989. Because his master pays it.
990. When both are at a railroad station.
991. Because heat expands things and cold contracts them.
992. A mare's.
993. A long march.
994. Because it only follows you in sunshine.
995. O X (ox).
996. A whisper.
997. Wear them in again.
998. Because you sweep out the dust and leave the room.
999. Because it is so easily broken.
1000. Milestones, because you never see two if them together.
1001. The "Lily" may fade and its leaves decay,
The "Rose" from its stem may sever,
The "Shamrock" and "Thistle" may pass away,
But the "Stars" will shine forever.